I0867547

Would You Rather?

Outer Space

EDITION

Would You Rather?

Outer Space

EDITION

Blast Off into a Hilarious Game
of Astronomical Fun

LINDSEY DALY

Z KIDS • NEW YORK

Would You Rather? Outer Space Edition is a book of hypotheticals. Don't try anything unwise or unkind.

Z Kids
An imprint of Zeitgeist™
A division of Penguin Random House LLC
1745 Broadway, New York, NY 10019
zeitgeistpublishing.com
penguinrandomhouse.com

ISBN: 9798217151257
Ebook ISBN: 9798217151240

Printed in the United States of America
1st Printing

Cover art by Gareth Williams
Interior art © by mhatzapa/Shutterstock.com,
Drawlab19/Shutterstock.com, balabolka/Shutterstock.com,
Lightkite/Shutterstock.com, In Art/Shutterstock.com,
Yura Batiushyn/Shutterstock.com, JosepPerianes/Shutterstock.com,
Leremy/Shutterstock.com, jesadaphorn/Shutterstock.com,
petite lili/Shutterstock.com
Book design by Erin Yeung
Typeset by Kim Scott
Author photograph © by Jocelyn Morales

The authorized representative in the EU for product safety and compliance is Penguin Random House Ireland, Morrison Chambers, 32 Nassau Street, Dublin D02 YH68, Ireland. https://eu-contact.penguin.ie

For Mom, Dad, and Christian.
Love you to the moon and back.

Also for Paul, Lucas, Pedro, Dani'el, Charles,
Robbie, and Raphael, because I said I would.

Contents

Introduction

Outer space—the universe beyond Earth's atmosphere—includes planets, stars, comets, black holes, galaxies, constellations, and more! Have you ever gazed at the night sky and wondered what—or even who—is out there? Whether you've seen a bright planet shining through the darkness or made a wish on a shooting star, you've probably been intrigued by the world beyond our own.

But space isn't just for astronauts! Blast off into endless laughter with friends and family as you play *Would You Rather? Outer Space Edition.* This book offers more than 160 questions about the mysterious place we call outer space.

These "Would You Rather?" questions are an excellent way to showcase your knowledge of all things celestial *and* extraterrestrial and are designed to start funny, thoughtful, and creative discussions. The questions are for kids ages 8–12, but they're sure to entertain the whole family. You never know what fascinating details you might learn about what and *how* other people think!

Would You Rather? Outer Space Edition is designed to be played as a game based on humor, logic, and overall creativity, with winners for individual questions, rounds, and the entire book. Here you'll find funny and thought-provoking scenarios revolving around space. Are you ready to launch your imagination and put your mind to the test? Now's the time to show off your critical thinking skills, have fun, and reveal your brightest ideas while playing *Would You Rather? Outer Space Edition*!

Rules of the Game

Get a group of friends or family members together for a game of wits and creativity. The more the better!

* The game is played in eight rounds, with twenty questions in each round.
* Players rotate the responsibility of being the "judge" and read the question aloud to the group.
* Players will then respond with an explanation and take turns sharing their answers.
* The judge of that round will choose the best answer based on humor, creativity, or logic. Write the winner's name in the space provided below the question and assign them one point. If only two people are playing, the judge (the player reading the question) assigns 1 to 5 points for the answer (5 being the best answer) and records it with the other player's name in the space provided below the question.

* When all players complete the round, tally up the points to determine the winner for that round.

* In the event of a tie at the end of a round, the players who are tied will answer the tiebreaker question. All remaining players will vote on the best answer. If only two people are playing, whoever makes the other player laugh wins.

* When all players complete the book, the winner of the most rounds is the champion!

ROUND 1

The Universe (and Everything in It)

Would you rather

name a planet

or

a galaxy?

WINNER: POINTS:

Would you rather

know the size of the universe

or

what happens in a black hole?

WINNER: POINTS:

Would you rather

be able to see dark matter
with your naked eye

or

run at the speed of light?

WINNER: POINTS:

Would you rather

walk on the moon

or

discover a way to land
on the sun?

WINNER: POINTS:

Would you rather
have witnessed
the big bang
or
travel to the end
of the universe?

WINNER: POINTS:

Would you rather
try to run in space
or
do somersaults?

WINNER: POINTS:

Would you rather

join the Guardians of the Galaxy

or

be a Jedi Knight?

WINNER: POINTS:

Would you rather

play baseball in zero gravity

or

jump rope?

WINNER: POINTS:

Would you rather

be able to breathe in space without a space suit

or

tolerate its subzero temperatures?

WINNER: POINTS:

Would you rather

live on a planet with no gravity

or

no natural light?

WINNER: POINTS:

Would you rather
travel back in time to
before the big bang
or
one million years
into the future?

WINNER: POINTS:

Would you rather
live on a planet in
the Milky Way
or
the Andromeda Galaxy?

WINNER: POINTS:

Would you rather

have X-ray vision after exposure to gamma rays

or

gain superhuman strength?

WINNER: POINTS:

Would you rather

travel through a black hole that leads to another universe

or

colonize a new planet?

WINNER: POINTS:

Would you rather
be able to travel at
the speed of light
or
manipulate time?

WINNER: POINTS:

Would you rather
spend 12 hours a day
floating in space
or
glued to Earth's surface?

WINNER: POINTS:

Would you rather

interview Neil Armstrong about the first moon landing

or

Katherine Johnson, who did the math to get him there?

WINNER: POINTS:

Would you rather

watch a rocket ship blast off

or

land?

WINNER: POINTS:

Would you rather
spend five years in space
or
one day?

WINNER: POINTS:

Would you rather
harness solar flares
to create energy
or
turn gravity off anytime
you want?

WINNER: POINTS:

TIEBREAKER

Would you rather

discover a new galaxy

or

a constellation?

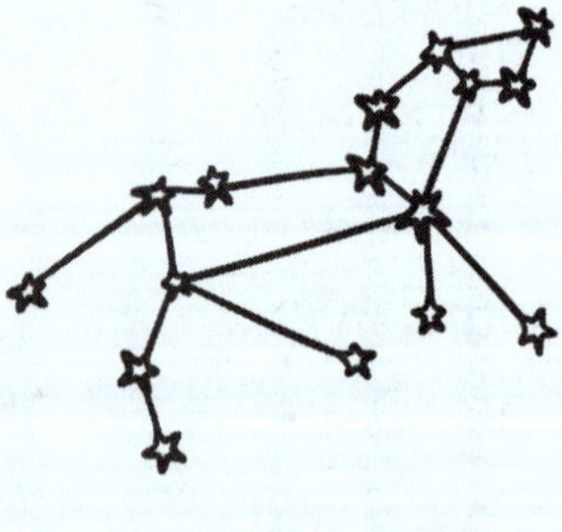

WINNER: POINTS:

WINNER

WINNER: ______________________

TOTAL POINTS: ______________________

ROUND 2

The Solar System

Would you rather

see a solar eclipse

or

a comet?

WINNER: POINTS:

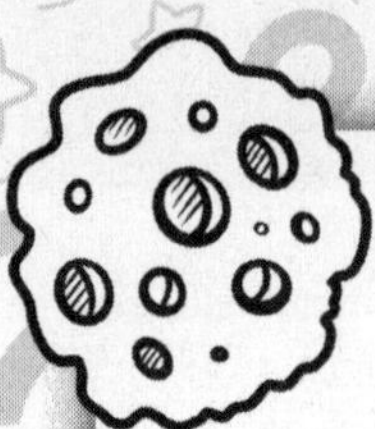

Would you rather

have a piece of a meteor

or

the moon?

WINNER: POINTS:

Would you rather

fly in a spaceship through the asteroid belt

or

a solar flare?

WINNER: POINTS:

Would you rather

orbit the sun

or

a planet?

WINNER: POINTS:

Would you rather
watch a meteor
shower every year
or
see Halley's Comet once?

WINNER: POINTS:

Would you rather
live on the moon
with your family
or
stay on Earth with
your friends?

WINNER: POINTS:

Would you rather

view a partial solar eclipse through a telescope

or

watch a total eclipse outside?

WINNER: POINTS:

Would you rather

see all the planets with your naked eye

or

every famous constellation?

WINNER: POINTS:

Would you rather
have a comet crash in
your backyard
or
an alien spaceship?

WINNER: POINTS:

Would you rather
stargaze in a dark field
or
visit a planetarium?

WINNER: POINTS:

Would you rather

witness the birth of a star

or

the death of a star?

WINNER: POINTS:

Would you rather

explore all the moons in our solar system

or

another planet that can support human life?

WINNER: POINTS:

Would you rather
view the sun's surface from
a fire-resistant spacecraft
or
travel to its core?

WINNER: POINTS:

Would you rather
see the sun burn out
or
grow to ten times
its current size?

WINNER: POINTS:

Would you rather

watch a meteor shower from the moon's surface

or

a spaceship?

WINNER: POINTS:

Would you rather

dissect a comet

or

a rock from another planet?

WINNER: POINTS:

Would you rather

see a shooting star every time you look at the night sky

or

a distant planet?

WINNER: POINTS:

Would you rather

watch a solar eclipse

or

a lunar eclipse?

WINNER: POINTS:

Would you rather

name asteroids in the asteroid belt

or

the moons of each planet?

WINNER: POINTS:

Would you rather

repel into a crater on the moon

or

hike around the rim?

WINNER: POINTS:

TIEBREAKER

Would you rather

see a solar flare close-up

or

a star go supernova
from a distance?

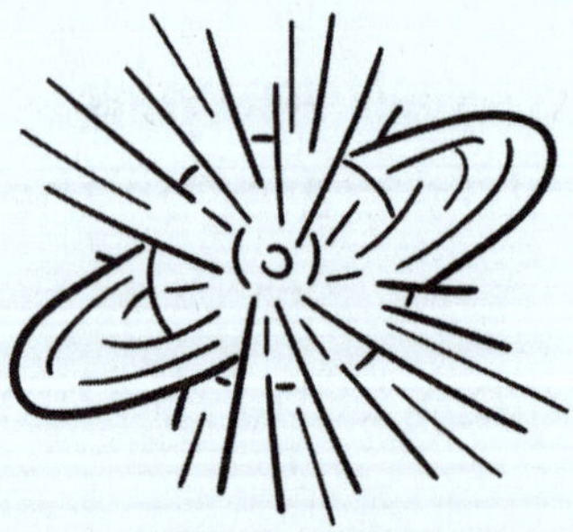

WINNER: POINTS:

WINNER

WINNER: ______________________________

TOTAL POINTS: ______________________________

ROUND 3

Earth: Our Place in Space

Would you rather
live on Earth and
look at the moon
or
live on the moon and
look at Earth?

WINNER: POINTS:

Would you rather
be immune to gravity
or
able to stare at the sun without
damaging your eyes?

WINNER: POINTS:

Would you rather
spend a night on the moon
or
in the middle of the ocean?

WINNER: POINTS:

Would you rather
take a bite out of the moon
or
the Earth's crust?

WINNER: POINTS:

Would you rather
experience all four seasons
or
only your favorite one?

WINNER: POINTS:

Would you rather
crash-land on Earth
from another planet
or
on another planet
from Earth?

WINNER: POINTS:

Would you rather
have solar flares fry your Wi-Fi connection
or
your lights?

WINNER: POINTS:

Would you rather
have a garden full of plants that don't require sunlight
or
water?

WINNER: POINTS:

Would you rather
look through a massive
telescope during the day
or
at night?

WINNER: POINTS:

Would you rather
be able to control
the sun's intensity
or
its position in the sky?

WINNER: POINTS:

Would you rather

be warned that a giant meteor was going to hit Earth

or

not know it was coming?

WINNER: POINTS:

Would you rather

live in a spaceship that orbits Earth for five years

or

live on another planet forever?

WINNER: POINTS:

Would you rather
work at NASA
headquarters
or
be an astronaut?

WINNER: POINTS:

Would you rather
live on Earth with double
the gravitational pull
or
no gravity at all?

WINNER: POINTS:

Would you rather

have Earth's atmosphere turn into a thick fog

or

have a foul odor?

WINNER: POINTS:

Would you rather

experience a yearlong rainstorm on Earth

or

a drought?

WINNER: POINTS:

Would you rather

have Earth spin faster

or

slower?

WINNER: POINTS:

Would you rather

live in a city riddled with smog

or

one that always floods?

WINNER: POINTS:

Would you rather
camp out under
a full moon
or
a crescent moon?

WINNER: POINTS:

Would you rather
swim in an ocean that has
constant giant waves
or
no waves at all?

WINNER: POINTS:

TIEBREAKER

Would you rather

go to space with a dog as your copilot

or

a monkey?

WINNER: POINTS:

WINNER

WINNER: ______________________________

TOTAL POINTS: ______________________________

ROUND 4

Our Planet Friends

Would you rather

visit the windiest planet

or

the dustiest planet?

WINNER: POINTS:

Would you rather

visit a planet with no oxygen

or

no water?

WINNER: POINTS:

Would you rather

have a planet named after you

or

a constellation?

WINNER: POINTS:

Would you rather

travel to the planet closest to Earth

or

the farthest away?

WINNER: POINTS:

Would you rather
live on a planet where
the sun never sets
or
never rises?

WINNER: POINTS:

Would you rather
paint a mural of the solar
system in your bedroom
or
a night sky full of stars?

WINNER: POINTS:

Would you rather

be stuck on another planet

with people you don't like

or

mysterious creatures?

WINNER: POINTS:

Would you rather

see the rings of Saturn up close

or

Jupiter's Great Red Spot?

WINNER: POINTS:

Would you rather
orbit a gas giant
or
an ice giant?

WINNER: POINTS:

Would you rather
live on Uranus with
21-year-long seasons
or
on Neptune with
1,200 mph winds?

WINNER: POINTS:

Would you rather

get caught in helium rain on Jupiter

or

in a dust devil on Mars?

WINNER: POINTS:

Would you rather

live on a planet with floating cities

or

where all of civilization is underground?

WINNER: POINTS:

Would you rather

study weather patterns on other planets

or

geography?

WINNER: POINTS:

Would you rather

teleport to the methane-frost-capped mountains of Pluto

or

the rust-colored deserts of Mars?

WINNER: POINTS:

Would you rather
design robots that collect samples from other planets
or
be an astrophysicist?

WINNER: POINTS:

Would you rather
live on a planet that has five moons
or
two suns?

WINNER: POINTS:

Would you rather
be named Pluto
or
Venus?

WINNER: POINTS:

Would you rather
live on the biggest planet
or
the smallest?

WINNER: POINTS:

Would you rather

explore every planet in our solar system

or

one exoplanet outside of it?

WINNER: POINTS:

Would you rather

visit the dormant Olympus Mons volcano on Mars

or

watch Earth's tallest volcano erupt?

WINNER: POINTS:

TIEBREAKER

Would you rather

walk across the lava fields
of Jupiter's moon

or

through Venus's
toxic winds?

WINNER: POINTS:

WINNER

WINNER: ______________________

TOTAL POINTS: ______________________

ROUND

5

Stunning Stars

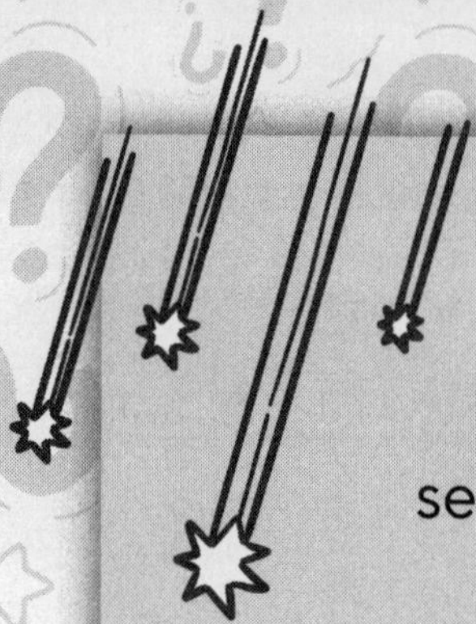

Would you rather

see a star explode

or

watch a meteor shower?

WINNER: POINTS:

Would you rather

find your way on a dark night
using the North Star as a guide

or

the Milky Way?

WINNER: POINTS:

Would you rather
get pulled into a
black hole
or
transported to a
different galaxy?

WINNER: POINTS:

Would you rather
spend a day sunbathing
or
a night stargazing?

WINNER: POINTS:

Would you rather

look through a telescope

at a nebula

or

a supernova?

WINNER: POINTS:

Would you rather

have a bad sunburn

on your butt

or

on the bottom of your feet?

WINNER: POINTS:

Would you rather
find the remains of a star that fell to Earth
or
have a star named after you?

WINNER: POINTS:

Would you rather
live as long as Earth
or
the sun?

WINNER: POINTS:

Would you rather

see the sun being formed

or

the first black hole?

WINNER: POINTS:

Would you rather

use the sun to
roast marshmallows

or

a star as a night-light?

WINNER: POINTS:

Would you rather

have all your wishes on a shooting star come true

or

get a penny for every star you see in the night sky?

WINNER: POINTS:

Would you rather

discover a way to land on stars

or

how to prevent stars from burning out?

WINNER: POINTS:

Would you rather

watch a live feed of the Milky Way for 24 hours straight

or

the sun?

WINNER: POINTS:

Would you rather

make a map of the night sky

or

count all the stars that are visible from Earth?

WINNER: POINTS:

Would you rather

watch a time-lapse of the birth of a random star

or

the sun?

WINNER: POINTS:

Would you rather

create a star in a lab

or

a nebula?

WINNER: POINTS:

Would you rather

stargaze under a perfectly clear, dark sky

or

view stars from an observatory?

WINNER: POINTS:

Would you rather

have a head shaped like a star

or

hands?

WINNER: POINTS:

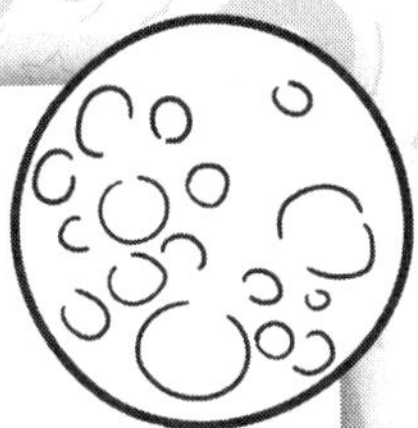

Would you rather

live in a world without stars

or

the moon?

WINNER: POINTS:

Would you rather

explore the center of the Milky Way

or

its outer edge?

WINNER: POINTS:

TIEBREAKER

Would you rather

watch two stars collide

or

a planet form?

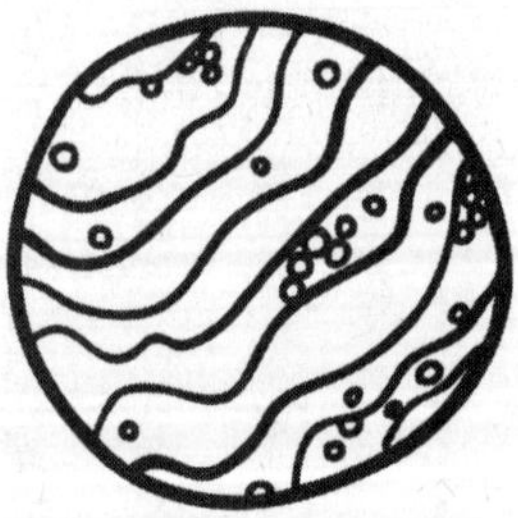

WINNER: POINTS:

WINNER: ____________________

TOTAL POINTS: ____________________

ROUND 6

Exploring Space

Would you rather
have your rocket ship land in the ocean after a trip into space
or
in a field?

WINNER: POINTS:

Would you rather
go on a mission with Buzz Lightyear
or
Han Solo?

WINNER: POINTS:

Would you rather

be a photographer for NASA

or

a scientist on a space station?

WINNER: POINTS:

Would you rather

sleep in one of the moon's craters

or

in a small space pod?

WINNER: POINTS:

Would you rather
watch a meteor shower through a telescope on Earth
or
through a window on the International Space Station?

WINNER: POINTS:

Would you rather
train for a space walk in an underwater tank
or
using virtual reality?

WINNER: POINTS:

Would you rather

design Mars Exploration Rovers

or

NASA rockets?

WINNER: POINTS:

Would you rather

watch a satellite launch into space

or

a spacecraft land in the ocean?

WINNER: POINTS:

Would you rather

receive a selfie from an astronaut

or

a text about their mission?

WINNER: POINTS:

Would you rather

build a rocket

or

a space plane?

WINNER: POINTS:

Would you rather
collect rock samples
from Mars
or
the moon?

WINNER: POINTS:

Would you rather
find a planet identical to Earth
or
a planet that's different but
also habitable by humans?

WINNER: POINTS:

Would you rather

pilot a space plane

or

a submarine?

WINNER: POINTS:

Would you rather

be an astronaut

or

a flight controller?

WINNER: POINTS:

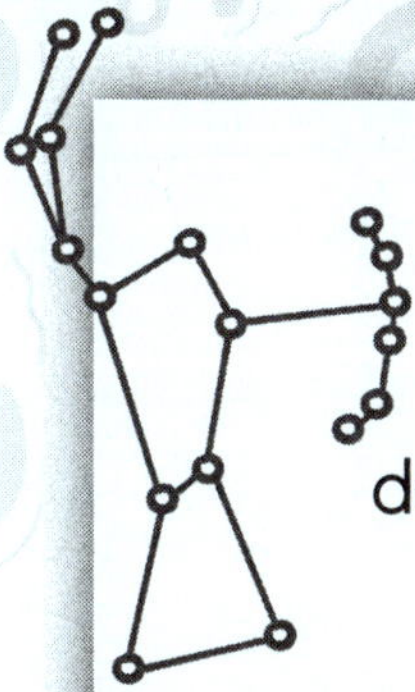

Would you rather

do a space walk through Orion's Belt

or

on the rings of Saturn?

WINNER: POINTS:

Would you rather

discover a planet where every living thing glows in the dark

or

sparkles?

WINNER: POINTS:

Would you rather

accidentally fly through
a black hole

or

the sun?

WINNER: POINTS:

Would you rather

travel to a galaxy
one million miles away

or

see Earth in one million years?

WINNER: POINTS:

Would you rather

control the Hubble Space Telescope for a day

or

a Mars Rover?

WINNER: POINTS:

Would you rather

leave a picture of yourself on the moon for future astronauts

or

a letter?

WINNER: POINTS:

TIEBREAKER

Would you rather

pilot a rocket

or

design a new International Space Station?

WINNER: POINTS:

WINNER: ______________________________

TOTAL POINTS: ______________________________

ROUND 7

Let's Live in Space!

Would you rather

live on one planet

or

visit all eight?

WINNER: POINTS:

Would you rather

live on the International Space Station floating through space

or

on a permanent base on Mars?

WINNER: POINTS:

Would you rather

be left behind on a space mission

or

leave someone else behind?

WINNER: POINTS:

Would you rather

be the first civilian to stay overnight in a space hotel

or

take a passenger flight to the moon?

WINNER: POINTS:

Would you rather
live on the International Space Station for six months
or
on Saturn for two?

WINNER: POINTS:

Would you rather
experience zero gravity for a month straight
or
30 random days?

WINNER: POINTS:

Would you rather

be a space tour guide

or

run NASA's social media?

WINNER: POINTS:

Would you rather

fly on a commercial space shuttle

or

accompany NASA astronauts on their spacecraft?

WINNER: POINTS:

Would you rather
be the first guest
in a space hotel
or
the last?

WINNER: POINTS:

Would you rather
live on a huge
space station alone
or
on a small space station
with friends?

WINNER: POINTS:

Would you rather

eat vacuum-packed food
for a year in space

or

meals you brought from Earth?

WINNER: POINTS:

Would you rather

be the first human born
on a distant planet

or

the first to retire on one?

WINNER: POINTS:

Would you rather
live in deep space
where it's dark
or
on the always sunny
side of the moon?

WINNER: POINTS:

Would you rather
live off astronaut ice cream
or
freeze-dried meat?

WINNER: POINTS:

Would you rather

wear a space suit every day for a year

or

gravity boots?

WINNER: POINTS:

Would you rather

stay in a floating hotel

or

in a glass dome on Mars?

WINNER: POINTS:

Would you rather

travel to space with
your family and friends

or

a group of trained
astronauts and scientists?

WINNER: POINTS:

Would you rather

fly through a meteor shower

or

a solar flare?

WINNER: POINTS:

Would you rather

live on a planet with
freezing temperatures

or

extreme heat?

WINNER: POINTS:

Would you rather

take a 2-week vacation
on the moon

or

another planet?

WINNER: POINTS:

TIEBREAKER

Would you rather

live on a planet where you can jump super high

or

see beautiful rings and moons?

WINNER: POINTS:

WINNER: ______________________

TOTAL POINTS: ______________________

ROUND 8

Anybody Out There?

Would you rather

be the first person to
contact extraterrestrials

or

find a flying saucer
in your yard?

WINNER: POINTS:

Would you rather

discover that there are hundreds of
humanlike species in the universe

or

that we are the only ones?

WINNER: POINTS:

Would you rather

be allowed inside Area 51

or

join a secret space mission to find extraterrestrials?

WINNER: POINTS:

Would you rather

be abducted by friendly aliens for a week

or

hide an alien in your room?

WINNER: POINTS:

Would you rather
discover a planet filled with creatures that look like plants
or
aliens that live underwater?

WINNER: POINTS:

Would you rather
meet an alien that is microscopic
or
gigantic?

WINNER: POINTS:

Would you rather

follow a UFO in a car

or

a helicopter?

WINNER: POINTS:

Would you rather

contact an alien species

or

be contacted by them?

WINNER: POINTS:

Would you rather

be friends with an alien

or

fly its spaceship?

WINNER: POINTS:

Would you rather

find alien technology

or

a book written in an alien language?

WINNER: POINTS:

Would you rather
tell one friend about
an alien encounter
or
tell the world and have to answer
endless questions about it?

WINNER: POINTS:

Would you rather
receive a message
from deep space
or
send one from Earth?

WINNER: POINTS:

Would you rather

encounter aliens that are covered in hair

or

tentacles?

WINNER: POINTS:

Would you rather

have Earth taken over by small, intelligent aliens

or

huge, dumb ones?

WINNER: POINTS:

Would you rather

tour an alien mothership

or

show a group of aliens around Earth?

WINNER: POINTS:

Would you rather

have an alien show up to your birthday party

or

be the only human at an alien's party?

WINNER: POINTS:

Would you rather

see a UFO up close by yourself

or

from a distance with a group of friends?

WINNER: POINTS:

Would you rather

compete against a team of giant aliens in basketball

or

soccer?

WINNER: POINTS:

Would you rather

discover a UFO crash site

or

crop circles?

WINNER: POINTS:

Would you rather

have an alien as a teacher

or

a doctor?

WINNER: POINTS:

TIEBREAKER

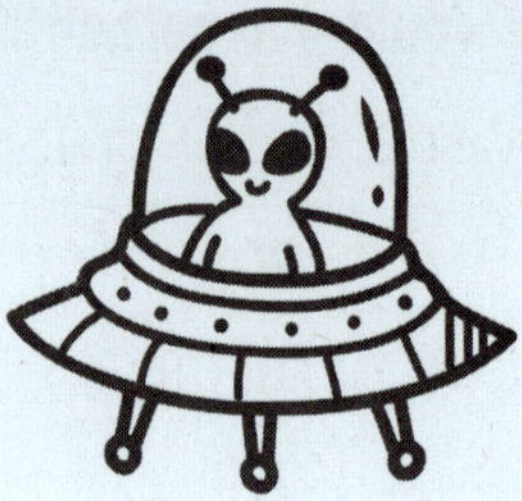

Would you rather

live in a spaceship

with aliens

or

on their home planet?

WINNER: POINTS:

WINNER: ____________________

TOTAL POINTS: ____________________

WINNER

This certificate
is awarded to

____

for having cosmic creativity,
a stellar sense of humor, and
logic that's out of this world!
You're a star!

CONGRATULATIONS!

About the Author

Lindsey Daly is a middle school social studies teacher and the author of the bestselling Would You Rather? series and card deck. She lives in New Jersey.

Parents, you can find her at:

@lindseydalybooks

@LindseyDaly10

Hi, parents and caregivers,

We hope your child enjoyed *Would You Rather? Outer Space Edition*. If you have any questions or concerns about this book, or have received a damaged copy, please contact customerservice@penguinrandomhouse.com. We're here and happy to help. Also, please consider writing a review on your favorite retailer's website to let others know what you and your child thought of the book!

Sincerely,
The Zeitgeist Team